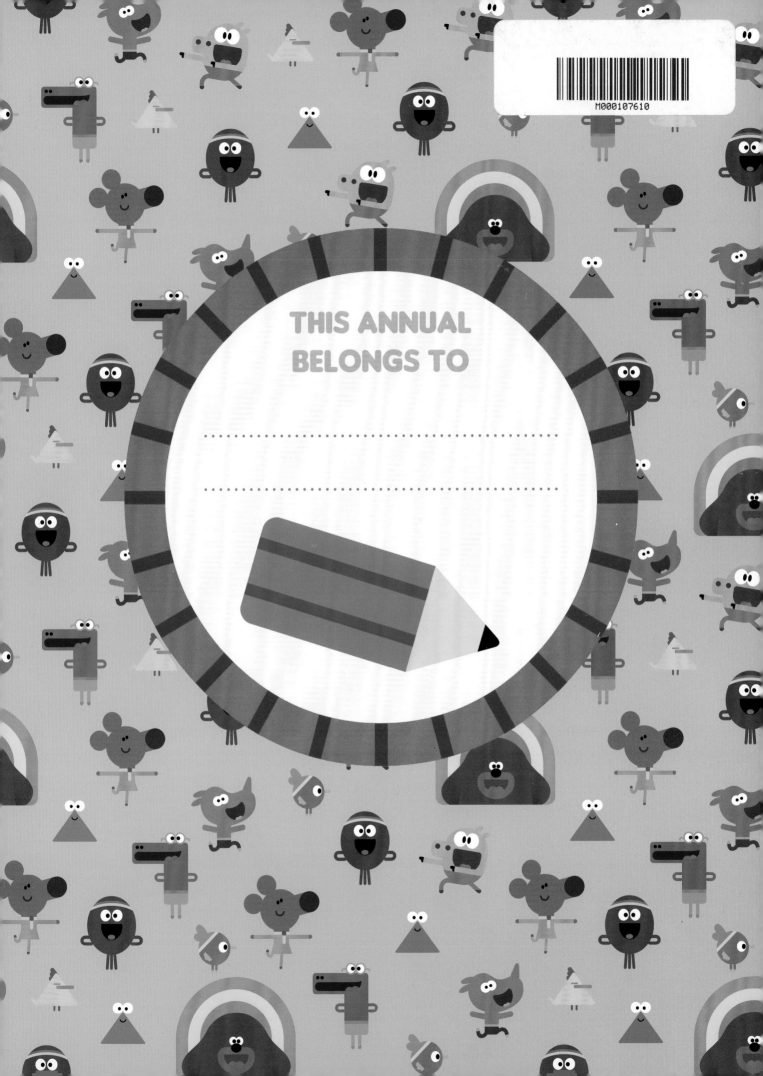

THIS ANNUAL
BELONGS TO

....

....

HEY DUGGEE

LADYBIRD BOOKS
UK | USA | Canada | Ireland | Australia | India | New Zealand | South Africa

Ladybird Books is part of the Penguin Random House group of companies whose addresses can be found at global.penguinrandomhouse.com.

www.penguin.co.uk   www.puffin.co.uk   www.ladybird.co.uk

Penguin Random House UK

First published 2022
001

Text and illustrations copyright © Studio AKA Limited, 2022
Adapted by Jane Kent

Printed in China

The authorized representative in the EEA is Penguin Random House Ireland, Morrison Chambers, 32 Nassau Street, Dublin D02 YH68

A CIP catalogue record for this book is available from the British Library

ISBN: 978-1-405-95078-7

All correspondence to:
Ladybird Books, Penguin Random House Children's
One Embassy Gardens, 8 Viaduct Gardens, London SW11 7BW

MIX
Paper from
responsible sources
FSC
www.fsc.org
FSC® C018179

DUGGEE

CONTENTS

BETTY

NORRIE

ROLY

TAG

HAPPY

SNOW MANY CREATURES

Duggee has built some frosty snow creatures. Draw lines to match the pairs before they melt.

 **1**

 2

 3

 A

 C

 B

 D

ONE ... TWO ... THREE ... THROW!

The Squirrels are ready for a fun-tastic snowball fight, but someone has already splatted Duggee! Which Squirrel was it? Count each pile of snowballs to find out.

HINT: EACH SQUIRREL STARTED THE FIGHT WITH FIVE SNOWBALLS.

ANSWER: Roly splatted Duggee with a snowball!

CHRISTMAS STOCKINGS

The Squirrels want to hang their stockings above the fireplace, but they're all mixed up! Trace the letters to work out which stocking belongs to which Squirrel.

1. N
2. T
3. B
4. R
5. H

DECORATE WITH DUGGEE

Duggee is busy decorating the Christmas tree.
Help him finish the job by matching the
missing jigsaw pieces to the picture.

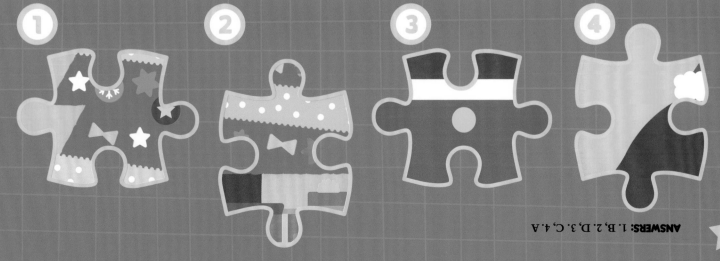

SQUIRREL BAUBLES

Decorate your Christmas tree with some very festive friends! Here's how to make six super Squirrel Club baubles.

YOU WILL NEED

 scissors glue  A4 card string

WHAT TO DO

SCISSORS ARE SHARP! ASK A GROWN-UP FOR HELP.

1. Ask a grown-up to help you cut out the opposite page.

2. Add glue to the back of the page, then stick it on to a piece of A4 card.

3. When the glue is dry, ask a grown-up to help you cut out the baubles, then make a hole at the top of each bauble.

4. Put a piece of string through the hole in each bauble, then tie the ends of the string together to make a loop. Now your baubles are ready to hang on the Christmas tree!

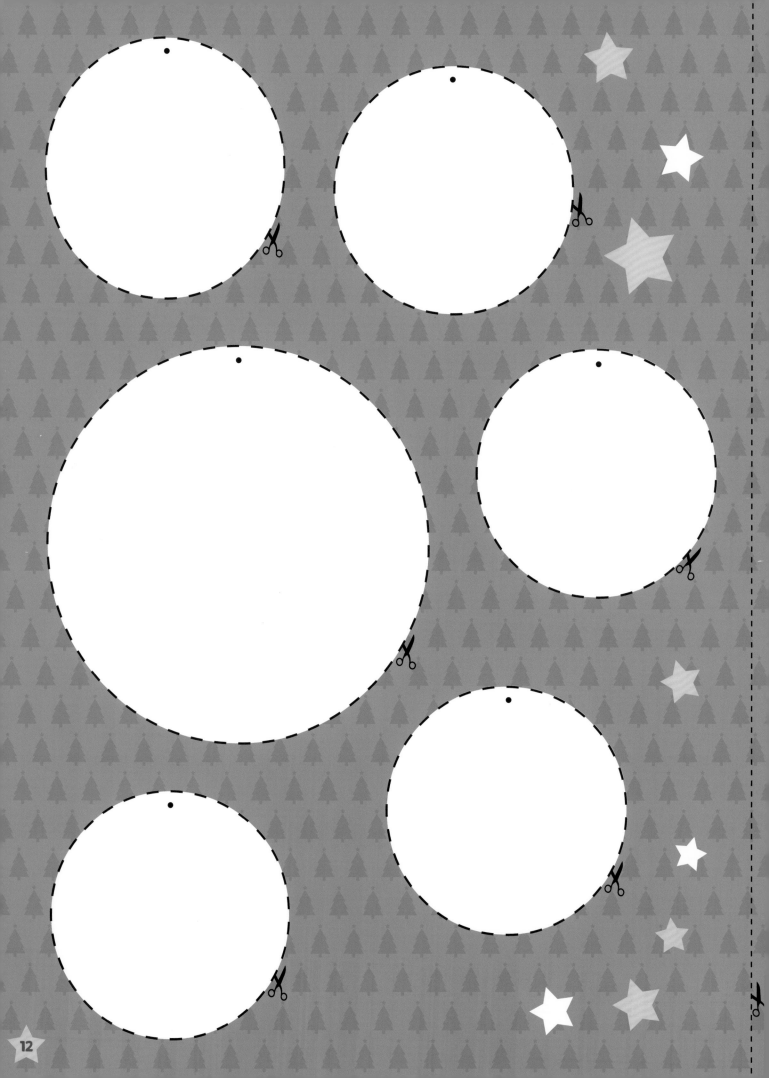

PRESENT PUZZLE

Shh! Santa Duggee has wrapped some presents for the Squirrels. Can you work out which Squirrel each gift is for?

Betty's present is the biggest.

Happy's present is the smallest.

Norrie's present is round.

Roly has already opened his present.

Tag's present is orange.

STORY TIME:

THE ART BADGE

The sun is shining, and Duggee and the Squirrels are relaxing in the garden.

"COMING THROUGH!" calls a loud voice.
"It's Tino the artistic mouse and his friends," says Betty.

The artistic woodpecker pins a poster to a tree.
"What's that for?" asks Happy.
"I'm putting on an art show," says Tino. "Anyone can enter!"

"Can we make some art for the show, Duggee?" asks Norrie.
"Ah-woof!" says Duggee. Of course they can!
"YAY!" shout the Squirrels.

There's one problem. The Squirrels don't know what to make.

ERR . . .

HMM . . .

Don't worry, Squirrels. Duggee can help. He has his **Art Badge!** What you need is inspiration. "Inspi-what?" asks Happy. Inspiration is anything that gives you an idea!

For example, inspiration could come from the materials you use, like pencils . . .

chalk . . .

paint . . .

or even collage!

"I'm inspired by collage!" says Norrie. She has used bits of paper and glue to make her artwork.

Some artists are inspired by their passions, like . . . carrots!

Or bananas!

"I know what I'm inspired by!" shouts Roly. "Potatoes!"

SPLAT!

SPLAT!

SPLAT!

Roly has painted a rock to look like a potato.

You can make art however you want. You can use your mouth . . . ears . . . nose . . . or trunk!

"Inspiration! Inspiration!" cries Betty. She sprinkles herself with glitter and flowers. "I AM art!"

BLING!

BLING!

BLING!

Sometimes, you can find inspiration by looking at someone or something – or even by looking at yourself!

"I have an idea!"
says Tag. He paints
a portrait of himself.
"Finished!"

Art can be realistic or abstract . . .

neat or messy . . .

small or BIG!
Art can be anything, as
long as it's from the heart.

"I know!" says Happy.
"I heart water!"
He splashes blue
paint everywhere.

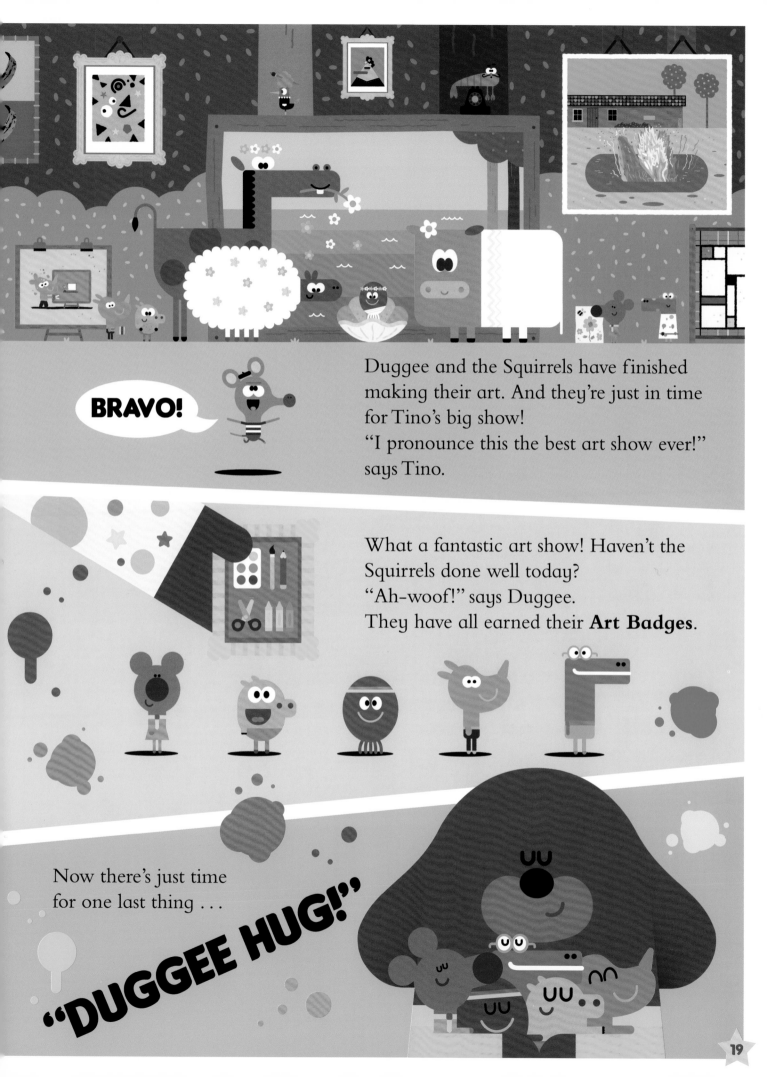

BRAVO!

Duggee and the Squirrels have finished making their art. And they're just in time for Tino's big show!
"I pronounce this the best art show ever!" says Tino.

What a fantastic art show! Haven't the Squirrels done well today?
"Ah-woof!" says Duggee.
They have all earned their **Art Badges**.

Now there's just time for one last thing . . .

"DUGGEE HUG!"

WILD ABOUT ART

Chew Chew the panda has created a beautiful painting! One of the pictures below matches it exactly. But which one?

① ② ③ ④

ANSWER: Picture 3 matches Chew Chew's painting.

BOUNCING ON THE BED

Ribbit! Frog has turned his bed into art!
And he's made quite a mess . . .
Can you answer the questions
about Frog's art?

1 What type of berry is on the floor?

2 How many blue bottles are there?

3 What's under the pink teacup?

4 What colour is the teapot?

ANSWERS: 1. It's a strawberry. 2. There are two blue bottles. 3. There's a penguin under the pink teacup. 4. The teapot is red.

21

YUM OR YUCK?

The Squirrels love to try new things – including new foods and drinks. But do they always taste yummy? Look at the Squirrels' faces to see if they like each new snack. Tick the box YUM if they do or YUCK if they don't.

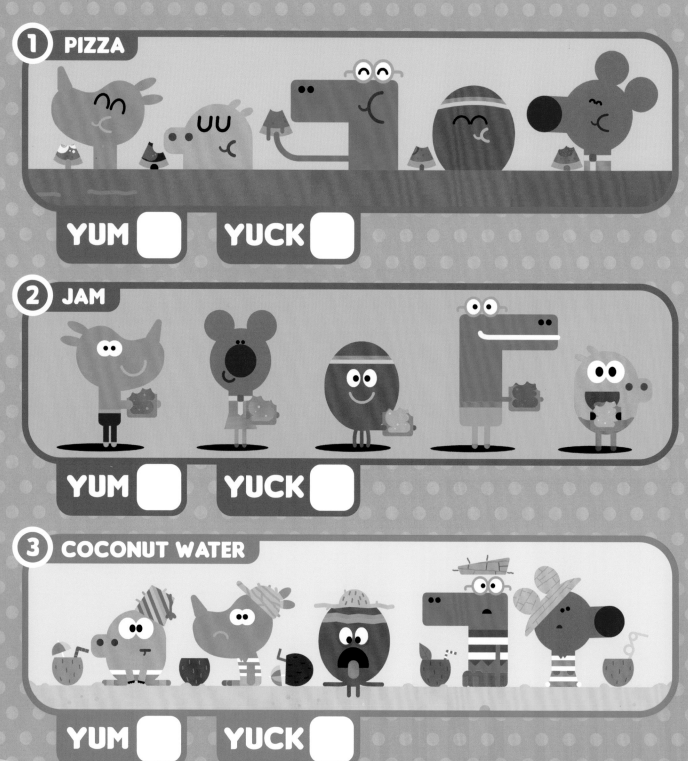

1 PIZZA

YUM ☐ YUCK ☐

2 JAM

YUM ☐ YUCK ☐

3 COCONUT WATER

YUM ☐ YUCK ☐

4 VEGETABLES

YUM ☐ YUCK ☐

5 FRUIT

YUM ☐ YUCK ☐

6 JUICE

YUM ☐ YUCK ☐

7 BANANA

YUM ☐ YUCK ☐

DANCING WITH STICK

Stick is dancing to the Stick song! But he keeps forgetting some of the steps . . . Can you help him remember them? Work out which dance move is missing from each row.

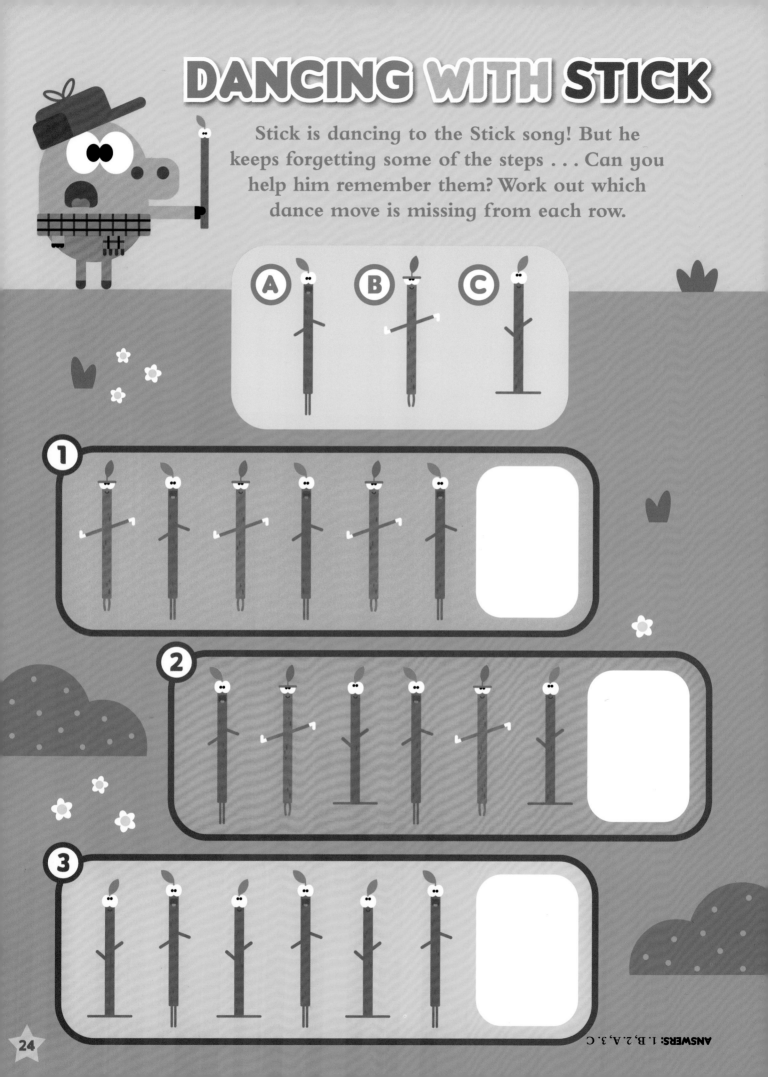

SUPER SHADOWS

Meet the Super Squirrels! It's time for them to zoom off to save the day. Can you match the superheroes with their shadows?

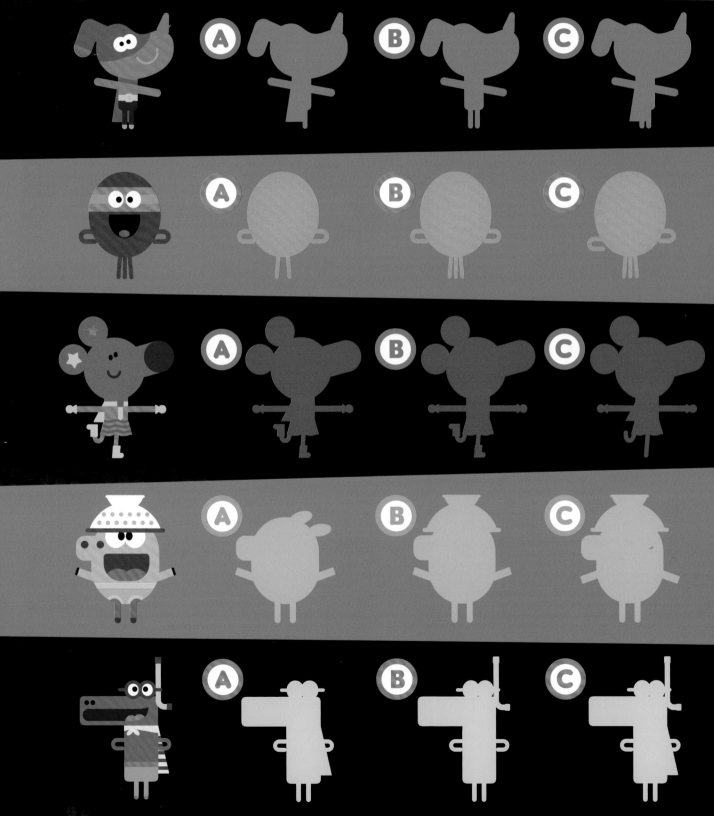

DUGGEE AND THE DINOSAURS

Duggee and the Squirrels have travelled back in time to visit prehistoric creatures! Join them on their journey by following the path and answering the questions along the way.

1 What is Happy using as a plate?

2 What colour is the flying dinosaur?

3 Who is in the cave painting?

26

5 How many green dinosaurs can you count?

4 What is the purple dinosaur wearing?

6 You've earned your **Fossil Badge!** Trace round the outline.

THE EGG ESCAPE

Bacaw! Bacaw! Oh no! Chicken has lost one of her eggs! Luckily, she numbered it with an even number. Which escaped egg is Chicken's?

POK!

2   6   8

7

5

4

1

3

ANSWER: Escaped egg number 4 is Chicken's.

SEEING SHAPES

Duggee is teaching the Squirrels all about different shapes. Can you help sort them into the box? Draw lines to link each shape with its matching hole.

BUG HUNT

The Squirrels love going hunting for bugs! You and a friend can go on a bug hunt too by playing this fun game. Get ready to draw some squares and spot some creepy crawlies.

YOU WILL NEED

 a friend

 two pencils

 scoring paper

HOW TO PLAY

Take turns drawing a line to connect two dots. You can only draw vertical or horizontal lines – no diagonals! If you complete a square when it's your turn, you get a point. If there's a bug inside your square, you get a bonus point!

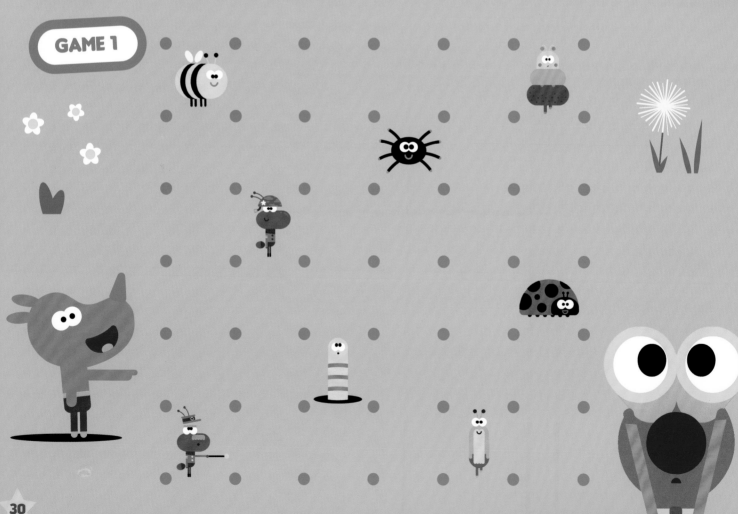

GAME 1

30

GAME 2

GAME 3

31

THE MAZE BADGE

The Squirrels are playing inside the clubhouse. But where's Duggee?

Duggee is in the workshop. "What are you doing, Duggee?" ask the Squirrels. "Ah-woof woof!" Duggee wants to clean up the workshop, but there's a problem. It's full of boxes!

"We'll help you, Duggee!" says Norrie. Once the workshop is empty, they'll be able to clean the floor.

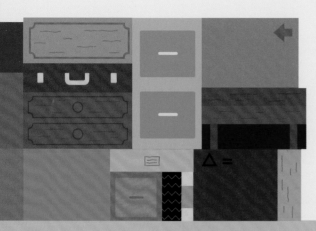

The Squirrels move box after box after box . . . until the boxes are piled up on the grass. At last, the final box is out. "Finished!" shout the Squirrels.

"Hey, where's Duggee?" asks Betty. The Squirrels can't see him anywhere!

"Duggee! Duggee!" the Squirrels call.
Duggee can hear them, but he can't see them. He is surrounded by boxes!

The Squirrels have made a maze with all the boxes, and Duggee is stuck in the middle!
"What's a maze?" asks Happy.

Duggee knows what a maze is. He's got his **Maze Badge!** A maze is a puzzle of paths and high walls. Most of the paths go nowhere, but one will take you to the middle of the maze – where Duggee is!

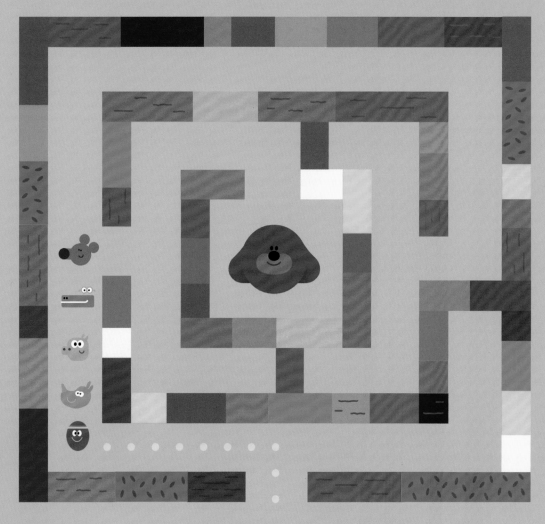

"Ooh! Stay where you are, Duggee," call the Squirrels. "We're coming to find you!" "Ah-woof!" says Duggee. Excited, the Squirrels enter the maze . . .

While the Squirrels search for the right path, Duggee settles down with a book and a cup of tea.

AHHHHH–WOOF!

"THIS WAY!" shouts Happy. The Squirrels follow along.

NO, THIS WAY!

The Squirrels turn round and go the other way.

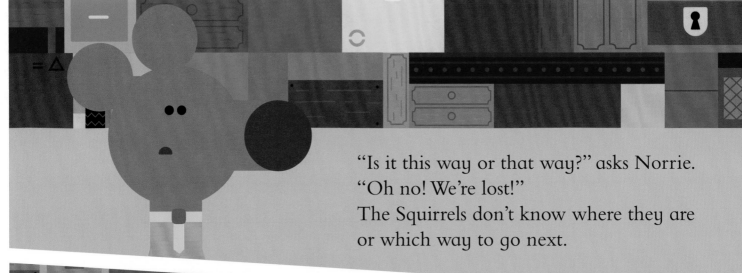

"Is it this way or that way?" asks Norrie.
"Oh no! We're lost!"
The Squirrels don't know where they are
or which way to go next.

Duggee has finished his book. Next, he gets out his trumpet and starts to play.

TOOT!

TOOT!

TOOT!

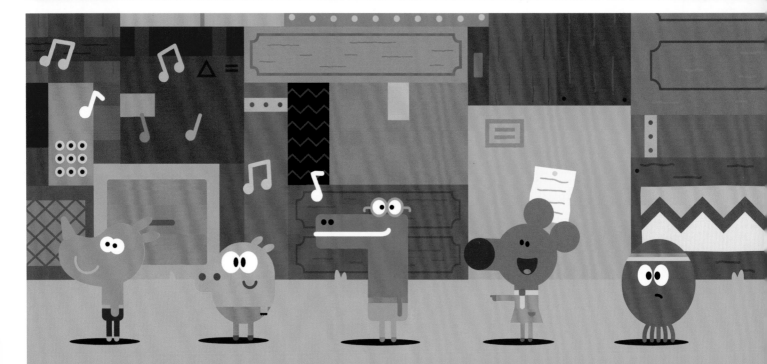

"What's that noise?" asks Happy.
"It's Duggee!" cries Norrie. "Let's follow the sound!"

The Squirrels follow the sound all the way to the middle of the maze. Well done, Squirrels! You've found Duggee. Now you just have to find the way back out . . .

Luckily, Duggee knows a quick and easy way. He has found a secret door that leads straight to the clubhouse.

Hooray! The Squirrels have earned their **Maze Badges**. Now there's just time for one last thing before the Squirrels go home . . .

"DUGGEE HUG!"

STARS AND SHELLS

The Squirrels have built a big sandcastle and decorated it with stars and shells. Put the decorations in size order from biggest to smallest.

BIGGEST ⬜ ⬜ ⬜ ⬜ ⬜ SMALLEST

ANSWER: E, A, B, C, D

REACH THE RAINBOW

Giddy-up! The Squirrel Club are travelling to the rainbow with their magical unicorn friend. Help them find the way through the maze – and watch out for fallen stars blocking the path!

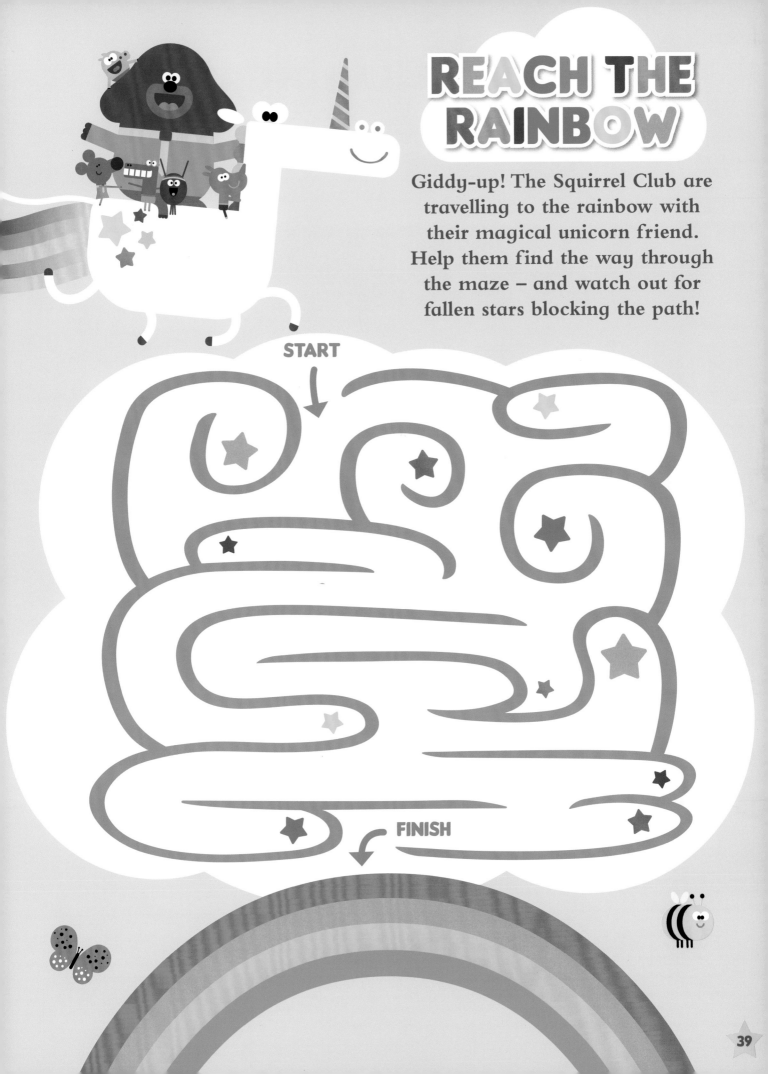

START

FINISH

TO THE CLUBHOUSE

Duggee can't wait to see the Squirrels today! Can you figure out which Squirrel has taken which path to the clubhouse? Trace each Squirrel's path with your finger.

ANSWERS: Tag – C, Betty – E, Norrie – A, Happy – A, Happy – A, Roly – B

ROLL UP, ROLL UP!

The Squirrels are excited because the circus is in town! There's so much to see. Can you spot all six things below? Tick each item off as you find it in the tent.

BLOWING BUBBLES

The Squirrels are blowing big, soapy bubbles . . . but they keep going POP!

How many times can you find the word "POP"?

6

POP

POP

POP

POP

POP

POP

A VERY COOL TRICK

Cosey the chameleon is really great at camouflaging himself!
Can you help him blend into these backgrounds? Copy the
patterns and colours with your colouring pens or pencils.

SQUIRREL CLUB PUPPET SHOW

Entertain your friends by putting on a fun Squirrel Club puppet show! Here's how to make your Squirrel puppets and a showstopping stage.

YOU WILL NEED

 scissors

 glue

 A4 card

 6 lollipop sticks

WHAT TO DO

1. Ask a grown-up to help you cut out the opposite page.

2. Glue the back of the page to a piece of A4 card.

3. When the glue is dry, ask a grown-up to help you cut out the Squirrels' faces and the stage curtains.

4. Fold the sides and bottom edge of the stage backwards along the dotted lines. Use the tabs to glue the side panels to the base so that the stage can stand up on its own.

5. Glue a lollipop stick on to the back of each Squirrel's face. Now you can move each Squirrel like a puppet!

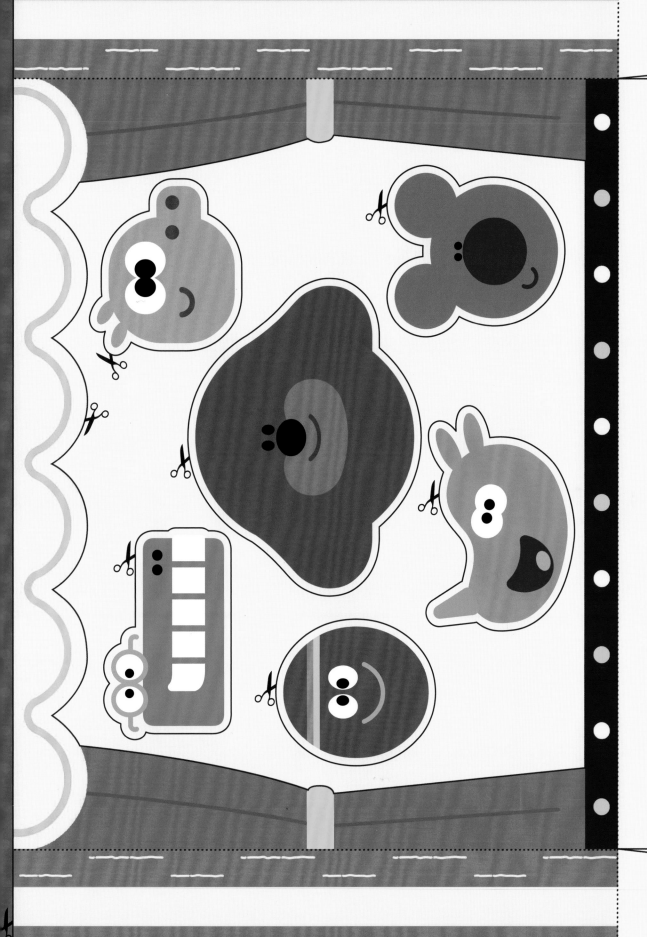

SNIP! SNIP! STICK! STICK!

The crafty Squirrels are making props for their own puppet show! But the craft table has lots on it . . . Can you help them spot the items they need? Tick each item off as you find it.

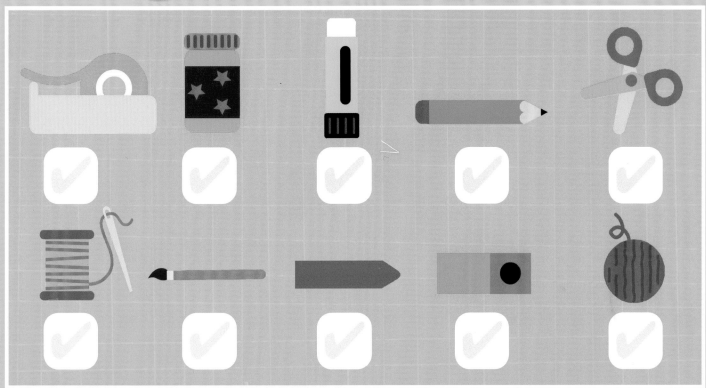

STORY TIME:

THE SUBMARINE BADGE

Duggee and the Squirrels are going on a trip to see Betty's dad, Ivor.

They're going to the pier next to the lighthouse! That's where Ivor has his submarine.

Ivor pops out of the submarine's hatch. "Oh, ho, ho. Hello, Squirrels! Hello, Duggee!" he says. "Hello, Dad!" says Betty. "Ah-woof woof!" says Duggee.

"Welcome aboard!" Ivor calls. "One at a time, through the hatch."
Wow, a submarine trip! How exciting, Squirrels!

Duggee's the last one in. Oops! He almost got stuck there for a moment!

UHH-WOOF?

"Are you ready for an underwater adventure?" Ivor asks the Squirrels. *Glug! Glug! Glug!* The submarine disappears beneath the surface.

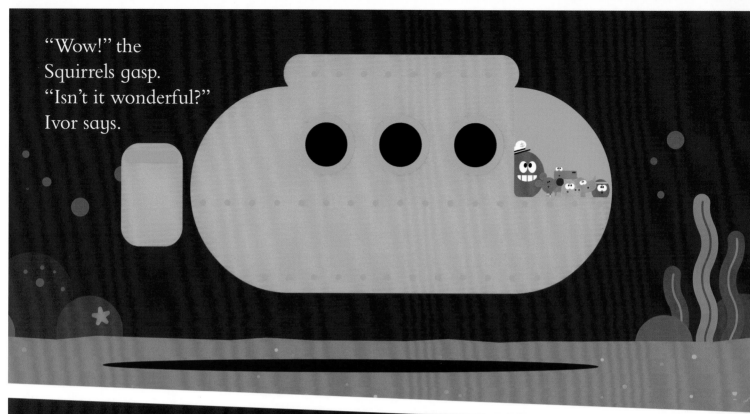

"Wow!" the Squirrels gasp. "Isn't it wonderful?" Ivor says.

Ivor gives the Squirrels a tour of the world beneath the waves. "Well, pickle my periscope! Jazz fish!" says Ivor. "You don't see many of them around."

"And look!" Ivor gasps. "There's a giant sea stallion too!"

NEIGH!

"This is Crazy Coral Junction," Ivor says. "Busy as always."

BEEP!

BEEP!

BEEP!

"Isn't it amazing, Squirrels?" says Ivor. "Squirrels?" He looks round. Where are the Squirrels?

Ivor finds the Squirrels exploring the submarine! Tag is looking through the periscope.

"Lovely to see you taking an interest, Tag," Ivor says. "But this is quite fragile . . ."

BEEP! BEEP! BEEP!

Happy is fascinated by the sonar. "Not too near the screen please, Happy," Ivor tells him.

"When the sonar makes a lot of noise like that, it means something is really close to the submarine," Ivor explains. "Let's go and see what it is!"

BEEP! BEEP! BEEP!

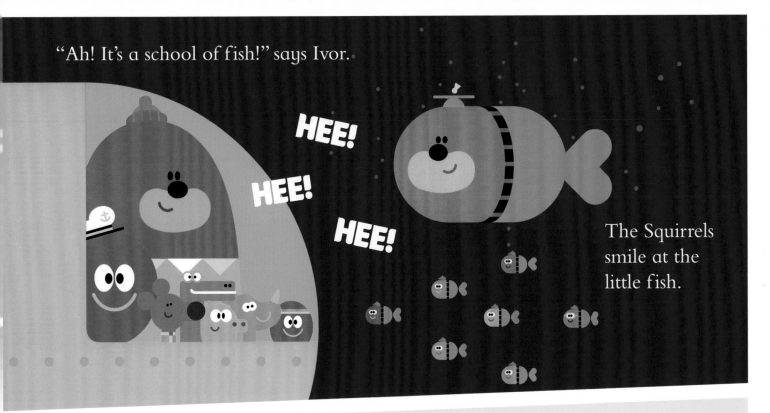

"Ah! It's a school of fish!" says Ivor.

HEE!

HEE!

HEE!

The Squirrels smile at the little fish.

"Right, now that you've made some new friends, it's time to head back to the surface," Ivor tells the Squirrels.

Back on dry land, the Squirrels say a big thank you to Ivor. Well done, Squirrels! You've earned your **Submarine Badges!** Now there's just time for one last thing . . .

"DUGGEE HUG!"

DEEP DOWN

The Squirrels are adventuring through the deep blue sea in their submarine. Trace the submarine's trail through the water using your pencil.

THE CAPTAIN'S CABIN

Ivor is showing the Squirrels around his
marvellous submarine. There's so much to see!
Can you spot six differences between the pictures?

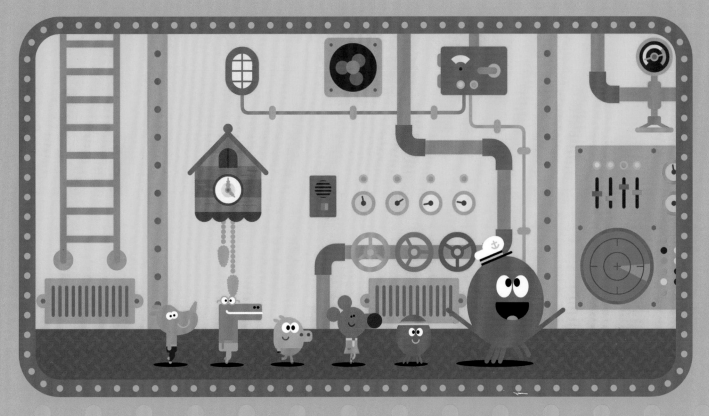

57

SPACE RACE

Join the Squirrels for an awesome space adventure! Who will be the first to race right round the galaxy and return to Earth?

7

8

9
YOU SWERVE ROUND A SATELLITE. ROLL AGAIN.

6
YOU SPIN THROUGH A SWIRL OF STARS. MOVE FORWARD TWO SPACES.

5

4
YOU STOP TO SAY HELLO TO AN ALIEN. MISS A TURN.

3

2

1

START

14

13

12
YOU WHIZZ PAST A COMET SHOWER! MOVE FORWARD TWO SPACES.

15
YOU SPOT A PLANET THAT LOOKS LIKE CHICKEN! GO BACK TWO SPACES.

16

17

11

19
YOU RACE THROUGH AN ASTEROID STORM. MOVE FORWARD TWO SPACES.

18

10

20

23
YOU PAUSE TO WAVE TO ASTRONAUT DUGGEE. MISS A TURN.

22

21

24

25

FINISH

SPIN AND SQUAWK

Norrie can't wait to take part in the Big Parade with her feathered friends. Just look at all the dancing birds! Can you spot the odd one out in each row?

1

A B C D E

2

U U U U U
A B C D E

3

A B C D E

4

A B C D E

60

DUGGEE HUG!

There's just time for one last thing before the Squirrels go home . . . Duggee Hug! Colour in the picture to complete it.

AH-WOOF!

HEY DUGGEE

LOOK OUT FOR THESE OTHER GREAT HEY DUGGEE BOOKS!

PICTURE BOOKS

BOARD BOOKS

HEY DUGGEE
THE BEDTIME BADGE

HEY DUGGEE
THE SPACE BADGE

HEY DUGGEE
THE SHARING BADGE

HEY DUGGEE
THE COLOUR BADGE

NOVELTY

HEY DUGGEE
HIDE AND SEEK
A LIFT-THE-FLAP BOOK

HEY DUGGEE
DINOSAURS
A LIFT-THE-FLAP BOOK

HEY DUGGEE
AH-WOOF!

HEY DUGGEE
ANIMALS
A TOUCH-AND-FEEL PLAYBOOK

DUGGEE AND FRIENDS LITTLE LIBRARY

STICKER ACTIVITY

HEY DUGGEE
MY POTTY BADGE
STICKER ACTIVITY BOOK
WITH POTTY REWARD CHART

HEY DUGGEE
DUGGEE'S DRESS-UP STICKER BOOK